The Best Of Alex 2010

Charles Peattie & Russell Taylor

Masterley Publishing

The Best Of
Alex
2010

First Published in 2010 by MASTERLEY PUBLISHING

Layout and Artwork: Suzette Field

ISBN: 978-1-8537578-3-9

Printed in the UK by CPI William Clowes Beccles NR34 7TL

Many happy returns to our sponsors.

2010 marks FTSE's fifteenth birthday, Mondo Visione's twentieth birthday, and this is the tenth *Best of Alex* collection they have jointly sponsored.

FTSE Group - provider of global equity, fixed income, alternative asset class, responsible investment & investment strategy indices; and Mondo Visione - the leading source of insight and knowledge about the world's exchanges and trading venues.

FOREWORD

Many thanks for buying this latest collection of Alex cartoons, as opposed to downloading them, having them delivered via an RSS feed or accessing them from a computer desktop widget. We're grateful for your support of this increasingly antiquated format - the "book" - and not just because it's one of the few modern media that people are still prepared to part with money for.

As cartoonists we are affected by more than just the rise of digital information delivery platforms. When we started in this industry we were the new kids on the block. Worryingly, nearly a quarter of a century later, we still appear to be. The baby-boomer cartoonists' generation we belong to (youngest member: our esteemed colleague Matt) have hogged the more desirable spots on newspapers for the last two decades and show no signs of giving way to younger competitors.

That's because there aren't any. Perhaps it's due to the failure of art schools to teach students to draw these days or the pre-eminence of stand-up as a comedy genre, but the cartoonists' environment has become an arid and inhospitable place, inimical to the emergence of new members of the species.

Those of us who are left see our natural habitat shrinking daily, now that almost all newspapers (apart from, at the time of writing, our own employer *The Daily Telegraph*) have become tabloids. Of course cartoons, being small and adaptable (like rats or cockroaches) will manage to survive, even if newspapers are reformatted to the size of paperbacks. But these changes bring unexpected challenges.

For example, shrinking newspapers and people's increasing use of digital media to access news have led to smaller headlines. In cartoons it is frequently useful to have a character reading a newspaper with a headline which flags up the topical reference in the gag. Trying to draw the same joke where the character is reading the news item on an iPhone with a screen only three inches tall presents logistical difficulties. Similarly, the fact that all London's evening papers are now freesheets has led to the disappearance from the capital's streets of another handy cartooning standby: the newspaper vendor's stand with the news story of the day written on it in bold capitals, which two cartoon characters can conveniently walk past while making some apposite and pithy comment. As if it wasn't already bad enough for our industry that rising sea levels from global warming will soon cause all the desert islands to disappear.

But for the moment we're still here and, more importantly, so are books. So we ask you to treasure this relic of a vanishing age. Lavish some care on it. Dog-ear the pages, break the spine, get coffee mug rings on it and install it lovingly in your downstairs loo. Next year it may only be available as a download for your iPad. The year after that it may be transmitted directly to a neural chip implanted in your brain.

And try showing a news item on <u>that</u> in a cartoon.

Charles Peattie and Russell Taylor

Alex - investment banker

Penny - Alex's wife

Rupert - senior banker

Clive - Alex's colleague

Bridget - Clive's wife

Cyrus - Alex's boss

Christopher - Alex's son

Sophie - Christopher's girlfriend

Vince - moneybroker

Hardcastle - Alex's client

Justin - Tory candidate

William - wealth manager

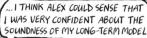

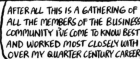

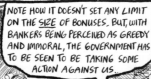

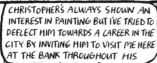

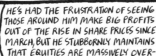

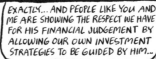

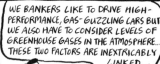

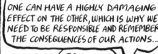

ALEX HOLIDAYED IN BRITAIN...

21

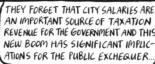

ALEX TOOK SICK LEAVE...

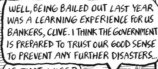

Alex PEATTIE + TAYLOR

LOOK, ALEX, YOU HAVE TO ACCEPT THAT PEOPLE MOVE ON IN THEIR CAREERS AND GET OFFERED JOB OPPORTUNITIES IN PASTURES NEW...

OF COURSE THEIR DEPARTURE CAN BE A GREAT BLOW TO SOMEONE LIKE YOU WHOSE DAILY BUSINESS DEALINGS HAVE FOR YEARS REVOLVED ROUND THEM...

THESE PROFESSIONAL RELATIONSHIPS CAN TAKE YEARS TO NURTURE, CLIVE...

AND IT'S SCARY HOW EASY IT IS TO BECOME DEPENDENT ON ONE INDIVIDUAL ...ESPECIALLY WHEN YOU PUT IN YOUR HABITUAL MORNING CALL ONLY TO BE TOLD HE NO LONGER WORKS THERE...

OH DEAR... HAS ALEX LOST A CLIENT?

NO... WORSE THAN THAT...

...A MAITRE D'...

NOW CHRISTOPHE'S LEFT "LA RENCONTRE" HOW AM I GOING TO GET THAT ALL-IMPORTANT CORNER TABLE UNDER THE MIRROR NEXT TIME I'M ENTERTAINING?

Alex PEATTIE + TAYLOR

THE GOVERNMENT IS PROPOSING TO BRING IN NEW LEGISLATION NEXT YEAR TO CURB CITY PAY...

SO WHAT? IT WON'T AFFECT THIS YEAR'S BONUSES.

ON THE CONTRARY, ALEX. CYRUS SAYS THIS IS A DIRECT THREAT TO THE FINANCIAL SECTOR NOT TO OVERSTEP THE MARK AGAIN - OR ELSE...

HOW ABSURD. CAN'T ANYONE SEE THIS FOR THE DESPERATE BLUFF IT CLEARLY IS...?

...A LAST PANICKED ROLL OF THE DICE FROM AN INCREASINGLY INEFFECTIVE AND FEARFUL REGIME AS IT MAKES A DOOMED AND FEEBLE ATTEMPT TO ASSERT ITS AUTHORITY...

WHAT, THE GOVERNMENT?

NO. THE BANK'S MANAGEMENT... TRYING TO GET OUR EXPECTATIONS DOWN NOW THAT WE'RE ALL FIRED UP FOR A BUMPER BONUS YEAR...

Alex PEATTIE + TAYLOR

SO, RUPERT, WHAT DO YOU MAKE OF THIS PROPOSED NEW GOVERNMENT LEGISLATION TO CURB BANKERS' PAY?

WELL, DAVID, ONE HAS TO REMEMBER THAT IT WOULDN'T COME INTO FORCE UNTIL NEXT YEAR AND IN ANY CASE IT WOULDN'T APPLY TO EXISTING EMPLOYMENT CONTRACTS...

TRUE.

BUT WHAT ABOUT ITS LIKELY EFFECT ON RASH, SELF-INTERESTED BEHAVIOUR BY BANKERS WHERE THEY PILE RECKLESSLY INTO DEALS, MOTIVATED BY THE PROSPECT OF IMMEDIATE PERSONAL GAIN?

OH THERE'S NO DOUBT ABOUT THAT.

I MEAN, THINGS ARE ALREADY WORSE THAN EVER... IT'S A HEADHUNTERS' FEEDING FRENZY OUT THERE...

WELL, IF PEOPLE ARE GOING TO JUMP SHIP SUDDENLY NOW'S THE TIME...

I'LL MEET YOU IN STARBUCKS IN 10 MINUTES...

CAN YOU CALL ME BACK ON MY MOBILE?

Alex PEATTIE + TAYLOR

THANKS FOR SETTING UP THIS JOB INTERVIEW FOR ME, SARA. IT'S ALWAYS HANDY TO HAVE A FEW OPTIONS ON THAT FRONT COMING UP TO BONUS TIME...

AS I DON'T KNOW MUCH ABOUT THE BANK IN QUESTION I SOUNDED OUT A FEW OF MY CLIENTS ABOUT THE PLACE. I'M AFRAID THEIR COMMENTS AREN'T VERY HELPFUL OR ENCOURAGING...

OH DEAR...

CLEARLY UNDER THE CIRCUMSTANCES I CAN'T LET MY POTENTIAL NEW BOSS KNOW WHAT THE POPULAR PERCEPTION OF HIS COMPANY IS...

WHAT, THAT IT'S WELL-RUN AND GENERALLY RESPECTED? CERTAINLY NOT.

I'VE GOT TO MAKE HIM THINK THAT I'M THE MISSING INGREDIENT HE NEEDS TO TURN THINGS AROUND...

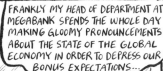

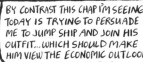

27

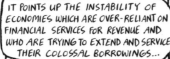

30

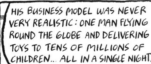

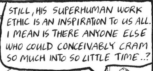

Alex PEATTIE + TAYLOR

THIS NEW ONE-OFF WINDFALL TAX ON BONUSES LEAVES BANKS IN A DIFFICULT POSITION...

DO WE GIVE OUR PEOPLE THEIR BONUSES AS USUAL AND PAY AN EXTRA 50% TO THE TREASURY OR DO WE RISK ALIENATING AND ANTAGONISING THEM BY ONLY PAYING HALF THE EXPECTED AMOUNT?

IT'S OBVIOUS, ISN'T IT? FRANKLY IF ANYONE MARCHES INTO MY OFFICE DEMANDING A BIG BONUS I TELL THEM TO TAKE A HIKE.

RIGHT.

...A SALARY HIKE?

QUITE. WE BUMP UP THEIR BASIC PAY FOR A YEAR AND THEN REDUCE IT AGAIN ONCE THE TAX NO LONGER APPLIES...

Alex PEATTIE + TAYLOR

2009 WAS A BAD YEAR FOR BANKERS. EVERYONE SEEMS TO HATE US...

THE CHANCELLOR TAXING OUR BONUSES, THIS NEW FRENCH E.U. COMMISSIONER APPOINTED TO REGULATE THE CITY, PROTESTORS AT THE G20 SUMMIT WITH THEIR "BURN A BANKER" PLACARDS...

IT'S DEPRESSING...

GOD KNOWS WHAT 2010 WILL BE LIKE..

WHAT DO YOU THINK CHRISTIAN? ARE BANKERS GOING TO BURN?

OUI, BIEN SÛR...

BERNE OR ZURICH... OR GENEVA... ANY OF THOSE PLACES LOOK GOOD RIGHT NOW...

Alex PEATTIE + TAYLOR

≥SIGH≤ IT'S BACK TO WORK TODAY, PENNY, AND A ROUTINE OF 7 AM STARTS AND LONG HOURS IN THE OFFICE...

BEEP BEEP...

5:10AM

THE CHRISTMAS BREAK WAS SUCH A WELCOME RELIEF FROM ALL THAT... AS I GET OLDER I FIND THE FESTIVE SEASON INCREASINGLY TINGED WITH NOSTALGIA...

IT ALWAYS BRINGS BACK FOND MEMORIES OF A BLISSFUL, IDYLLIC EXISTENCE BACK IN THE CAREFREE DAYS WHEN THE WORLD WAS A SIMPLER AND HAPPIER PLACE...

THAT'S ALL VERY WELL, ALEX...

BUT DOES IT MEAN YOU ALWAYS HAVE TO VOLUNTEER TO MAN YOUR OFFICE BETWEEN XMAS AND NEW YEAR?

GETTING IN LATE, TAKING A LONG LUNCH, SLOPING OFF AT 4·15.... JUST LIKE BACK IN THE 80'S...

Alex PEATTIE + TAYLOR

WHEN THIS LABOUR GOVERNMENT CAME TO POWER WE THOUGHT THEY WERE ATTUNED TO THE VALUES OF THE CITY...

BUT NOW THEY'VE EMBARKED ON A PUNITIVE TAXATION REGIME ON EXECUTIVE BONUSES THAT MAKES THE SUPER TAX OF THE 1960'S PALE IN COMPARISON...

ARE THEY NOT CONSCIOUS OF THE DANGERS OF ALIENATING THE CITY?

WELL, I SUPPOSE THEY RECKON THEY'VE COCKED UP THE ECONOMY SO BADLY THAT THEY WON'T GET RE-ELECTED...

EXACTLY...

SO SHOULDN'T THEY BE FOCUSED ON LANDING THEMSELVES SOME NICE, CUSHY ADVISORY ROLES WORKING FOR BANKS...?

I MEAN, WHAT ELSE DO WASHED-UP POLITICIANS DO WITH THEIR CAREERS?

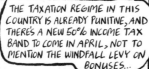

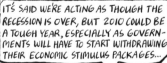

35

36

Panel 1: OF COURSE WHAT I'M WORRIED ABOUT IS MY CAREER BEING AFFECTED BY THE "GLASS CEILING".

REALLY?

SORRY, I COULDN'T HELP OVERHEARING.

Panel 2: AND I AGREE...IT'S A HUGE PROBLEM... THESE ARBITRARY BARRIERS WHICH CAN PREVENT PEOPLE LIKE ME FROM PROSPERING IN THE CORPORATE WORLD SHOULD HAVE NO PLACE IN THE 21st CENTURY...

EXACTLY.

Panel 3: WHY SHOULD I HAVE TO PUT UP WITH AN OUT-DATED AND DISCRIMINATORY ATTITUDE THAT SEEKS TO EXCLUDE ME FROM ACHIEVING MY LEGITIMATE PROFESSIONAL GOALS?

AS A WOMAN?

ER...NO...

Panel 4: AS A BANKER... YOU *WERE* TALKING ABOUT GLASS-STEAGALL, RIGHT?

ER...NO... "GLASS CEILING"...

OH THAT? NAH, I'M MORE WORRIED ABOUT ALL THIS OLD-FASHIONED BANKING LEGISLATION OBAMA WANTS TO BRING BACK...

Panel 1: AND HOW'S YOUR SON CHRISTOPHER GETTING ON?

WELL HE'S LIVING IN A SH*T-HOLE IN A GHASTLY PART OF TOWN BUT HE'S BEING AN ARTIST AND SECRETLY I RATHER RESPECT WHAT HE'S DOING...

Panel 2: THE POINT OF ARTISTS IS THEY LIVE LIKE THAT, ON THE EDGE, IN ORDER TO FUNCTION PROPERLY AND DO WHAT MAKES THEM IMPORTANT TO SOCIETY...

Panel 3: IT'S THE WAY CHRISTOPHER AND HIS ILK CAN ACTUALLY CREATE SOMETHING OF LASTING VALUE THAT LIVES ON AFTER THEM...

REALLY? LIKE WHAT?

Panel 4: WELL, A PROPERLY GENTRIFIED NEIGHBOURHOOD; IF ENOUGH OF THEM MOVE THERE, IN TWENTY YEARS' TIME IT'LL BE OKAY FOR PROPER PEOPLE LIKE BANKERS... AND THERE'LL BE GIFT SHOPS AND DELICATESSENS ETC...

PRIDE

AND THE ARTISTS WILL BE PRICED OUT?

WELL YES...

Panel 1: YOU'RE TAKING YOUR BANK'S WEIGHT LOSS COMPETITION VERY SERIOUSLY, ALEX. I HEAR YOU'VE GIVEN UP DRINKING.

Panel 2: WELL, I'VE CUT DOWN HEAVILY CERTAINLY, WHICH HAS COME AS A SHOCK TO THE SYSTEM. OBVIOUSLY MUCH OF LIFE OUTSIDE THE OFFICE IN THE CITY REVOLVES AROUND ALCOHOL...

Panel 3: AND NOW WORD'S GOT OUT ABOUT MY NEW ABSTEMIOUS REGIME IT'S AFFECTED MY DESIRABILITY AS A SOCIAL COMPANION IN THE AFTER WORK DRINKS SESSIONS...

SO I NOTICE...

Panel 4: YOU'RE MORE POPULAR THAN EVER...

WELL NOW THAT I ONLY PERMIT MYSELF ONE UNIT IT HAS TO BE OF THE HIGHEST QUALITY, WHICH MEANS IT'S NOT SOLD BY THE GLASS. A LYNCH-BAGES AND WE GET TO FINISH THE BOTTLE.

CHEERS...

Panel 1: MANY PEOPLE ARE SEEING THE MOVIE "AVATAR" AS A PARABLE OF THE MODERN GLOBAL ECONOMIC ORDER...

Panel 2: GREEDY RAPACIOUS CAPITALISTS (I.E.: US BANKERS) RECKLESSLY PLUNDER AND DESTROY THE NATURAL WORLD (IE: EVERYONE ELSE) FOR OUR OWN SELFISH, UNSCRUPULOUS ENDS...

OH REALLY?

Panel 3: YOU SHOULD SEE IT, ALEX. IT'S A FANTASTICALLY POWERFUL AND SUGGESTIVE FILM. MANY OF US DREAM OF LIVING IN THE 3-D WORLD IT EVOKES...

Panel 4: OOPS. LOOKS LIKE WE REALLY SCREWED UP THIS TIME...

YIKES!

UK CREDIT RATING DDD

ZZZ...

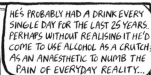

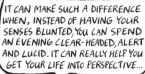

40

Alex — PEATTIE + TAYLOR

THE BANK'S WEIGHT-LOSS COMPETITION IS JUST A BIT OF FUN BUT IT CAN BE INSTRUCTIVE FOR OUR BOSSES...

AFTER ALL AN EXERCISE LIKE THIS HIGHLIGHTS AN EMPLOYEE'S CAPABILITY FOR STRATEGIC PLANNING, SETTING TARGETS AND ACHIEVING GOALS, WHICH CAN HELP DECIDE THEIR FATE WHEN REDUNDANCIES LOOM...

OF COURSE SOME OF OUR COLLEAGUES FAILED ABYSMALLY IN THE CONTEST. SOME EVEN MANAGED TO PUT _ON_ WEIGHT... LIKE VANESSA...

YES...

SO _HER_ JOB'S SAFE THEN...

QUITE. THE BANK WOULDN'T BE ABLE TO TAKE THE RISK OF FIRING HER IN CASE SHE TURNED OUT TO BE PREGNANT...

Alex — PEATTIE + TAYLOR

AS SOMEONE WHO'S WORKED FOR REGAL BANK OF CALEDONIA FOR MANY YEARS, ALEX, I REALLY RESENT THE WAY OUR BONUSES ARE BEING REPORTED IN THE MEDIA...

THE IMAGE OF BANKERS IN STATE-OWNED BANKS IS BEING SYSTEMATICALLY DEGRADED TO THE GENERAL PUBLIC, AND FINANCIAL DETAILS ARE BEING PRESENTED IN A HIGHLY-SELECTIVE AND UNFAIR WAY...

I MEAN, LOOK AT THIS, ALEX...

BUSINESS
TAX PAYERS' MONEY USED TO CREATE 100 NEW MILLIONAIRES

OH DEAR...

"NEW MILLIONAIRES"?! I'VE BEEN A MILLIONAIRE FOR _YEARS_ AND A CRUMMY LITTLE SIX-FIGURE BONUS WILL IN _NO WAY_ BE ENOUGH TO BRIBE _ME_ INTO STAYING ON THERE...

B*ST*RDS...

Alex — PEATTIE + TAYLOR

I SEE FROM MY FILES THAT IT'S THE BIRTHDAY OF THE DAUGHTER OF ONE OF MY CLIENTS TODAY... THAT GIVES ME AN EXCUSE TO PHONE HIM...

HOW NAUSEATING...

THAT SORT OF SYCOPHANTIC BEHAVIOUR JUST WORKS AGAINST YOU IN THE LONG RUN, CLIVE...

NONSENSE. I'VE BEEN DOING IT FOR YEARS. IT KICKS OFF THE CONVERSATION AND THEN WE CAN TALK ABOUT BUSINESS...

HI, BILL... IT'S CLIVE... HOW ARE YOU DOING? I WAS JUST THINKING: ISN'T IT CAMILLA'S BIRTHDAY TODAY?... SHE MUST BE SO GROWN UP NOW... HOW OLD IS SHE? SIXTEEN?... WOW...

ER, AN INTERNSHIP...? HERE...? ER, ER, SORRY, I'VE GOT AN URGENT CALL ON THE OTHER LINE I REALLY MUST TAKE...

CLICK

IDIOT... I DID WARN HIM...

Alex — PEATTIE + TAYLOR

IT'S TRUE THAT MANY OF US AT REGAL BANK OF CALEDONIA WERE PAID BIG TAXPAYER-FUNDED BONUSES LAST WEEK, ALEX...

BUT THEY WERE TO INCENTIVISE US TO DO THE VITAL WORK OF RE-BUILDING THE BANK'S SHATTERED BUSINESS... AND, REMEMBER, THE BONUSES WERE PAID 75% IN STOCK...

OBVIOUSLY THIS LINKS OUR FUTURE REMUNERATION TO GROWTH IN THE BUSINESS... WELL, I CAN TELL YOU, YOU WON'T FIND ANYONE MORE BULLISH AND POSITIVE ABOUT THE BANK'S OUTLOOK THAN ME...

YES...

I HEAR YOU'VE BEEN SAYING THAT TO EVERY PROSPECTIVE NEW EMPLOYER YOU'VE BEEN INTERVIEWING WITH...

WELL I NEED THEM TO BUY OUT MY BONUS SO I'VE GOT TO IMPLY I THINK IT'S GOING TO BE WORTH SOMETHING ONE DAY...

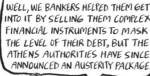

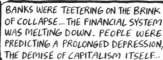

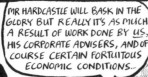

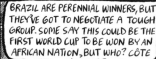

48

ALEX WENT ON HOLIDAY TO GREECE..

Alex PEATTIE + TAYLOR

It's ten years since the dotcom crash, but the internet has revolutionised the business world since then...

In the pre-digital days we'd have just a few analysts' notes available to us, but today we can tap into insiders' blogs, online market reports, all sorts of financial and economic analysis...

So whereas previously we were only getting a narrow idea of the thinking on a subject, nowadays we have access to the full range of opinions and insights...

RIGHT.

And as we now know that they all inevitably end up contradicting one another, we can save time by not bothering to read ANY of them.

IT'S MOST HANDY...

Alex PEATTIE + TAYLOR

You're a brave man, Justin, swapping your job at the bank to stand as a political candidate...

ACTUALLY I THINK I'M IDEALLY EQUIPPED, CLIVE..

Well, you may understand economics, but we live in times where the electorate is very factionalised... Even if you do win, you could only hope to get, what, 35% of the vote?

How does it feel to know that whatever you do or say, 65% of the public is going to be fundamentally hostile to you and everything you stand for?

NOT SO BAD.

After all it's a step up from being a banker, where the public hostility rate is closer to 95%...

THAT MUST BRING SOME COMFORT...

Alex PEATTIE + TAYLOR

So what made you decide to stand as a candidate in the election, Justin?

IT WAS THE MP'S EXPENSES SCANDAL, I SUPPOSE...

I was shocked and appalled by our politicians and thought I could do a better job... After all the main problem facing the country is the budget deficit...

Clearly we need to revitalise the private sector, which is where my expertise as a banker comes in... We have to forge links with local businesses and industry...

So I'll fix up a few meetings with them... That way I can claim the cost of all my first class travel and accommodation up there on expenses from the bank.

THAT'LL BE HANDY TO FALL BACK ON IF YOU DON'T GET IN...

Alex PEATTIE + TAYLOR

The problem with our election campaign is that it's all based on attacking the opposition...

We're constantly dwelling on the failings of the current government and how its mismanagement of the economy caused the worst recession in 80 years...

But instead of just banging on about the negative consequences of Labour's economic cock-ups, couldn't we focus on something more positive?

What, like the fact that we got this nice cheap constituency office in a shop that went bankrupt last year?

ACTUALLY I MEANT SOME POLICIES OF OUR OWN...

Strip 1:

Alex — PEATTIE + TAYLOR

Panel 1: THIS FLIGHT BAN DUE TO VOLCANIC ASH HAS CAUSED TRANSPORT CHAOS ACROSS EUROPE...

Panel 2: THEY SAY IT COULD TAKE WEEKS TO SORT OUT... ALEX IS A FREQUENT BUSINESS TRAVELLER... WAS HE BADLY AFFECTED? / HAPPILY FOR HIM HE GOT A TIP-OFF THAT PLANES WERE LIKELY TO BE GROUNDED.

Panel 3: FACED WITH THE PROSPECT OF ALL TRAVEL ANYWHERE IN EUROPE BEING BADLY HIT HE USED ALL HIS POWERS OF PERSUASION AND PROFESSIONAL INFLUENCE TO GET HIMSELF ON A FLIGHT... / WHERE DID HE NEED TO GET TO?

Panel 4: NOWHERE REALLY, BUT HE HURRIEDLY ARRANGED A LAST-MINUTE BUSINESS TRIP TO MILAN, THUS LEAVING HIMSELF "STRANDED" IN THE ALPS FOR THE LAST WEEK OF THE SKIING SEASON... / OH YES... HE'S JUST EMAILED ME A PHOTO OF HIS CHALET..

Strip 2:

Alex — PEATTIE + TAYLOR

Panel 1: I CAN'T BELIEVE WHAT'S HAPPENED: BEING STUCK OUT HERE ON HOLIDAY BECAUSE OF THE FLIGHT BAN...

Panel 2: I SHOULD HAVE GOT BACK TO THE OFFICE FIRST THING ON MONDAY MORNING BUT OF COURSE THAT'S COMPLETELY UNFEASIBLE DUE TO THE TOTAL SUSPENSION OF ALL U.K. AIR SERVICES...

Panel 3: IT SEEMS SO WRONG AND UNFAIR BEING CAUGHT OUT LIKE THIS... STRANDED AND UNABLE TO GO BACK TO WORK... / I KNOW...

Panel 4: ESPECIALLY SINCE WE'RE ONLY IN THE LAKE DISTRICT.. / YES, BUT I TOLD EVERYONE WE WERE GOING SKIING IN COLORADO... I CAN'T BLOW MY COVER NOW... / DAMMIT...

Strip 3:

Alex — PEATTIE + TAYLOR

Panel 1: THIS TOWN APPEARS TO ENJOY A HEALTHY EMPLOYMENT LEVEL BUT ACTUALLY IT'S AN ILLUSION... / FUND RAISING EVENT

Panel 2: SINCE THE LAST FACTORIES IN THE AREA CLOSED IN THE 90'S, MOST JOBS ARE IN THE PUBLIC SECTOR, SO THE STATE IS ACTUALLY PAYING PEOPLE TO WORK HERE... NO ONE GENERATES ANY REAL MONEY...

Panel 3: FRANKLY THE ONLY GENUINE INJECTION OF CASH INTO THE LOCAL ECONOMY COMES FROM AFFLUENT INDIVIDUALS LIKE JUSTIN THERE WHO'S STAYING IN A LOCAL HOTEL WHILE HE CONTESTS THE ELECTION...

Panel 4: SO, JUSTIN, DID YOU MENTION THAT YOU'VE BUILT UP SO MANY LOYALTY POINTS IN THE HOTEL CHAIN IN ALL YOUR BUSINESS TRAVEL FOR THE BANK THAT THE HOTEL IS EFFECTIVELY PAYING YOU TO STAY THERE? / I THOUGHT IT BEST NOT TO...

Strip 4:

Alex — PEATTIE + TAYLOR

Panel 1: WE ONLY HAD A LIMITED BUDGET FOR FITTING OUT OUR CONSTITUENCY OFFICE... / CAMPAIGN H.Q

Panel 2: WE COULD EITHER SPEND THE MONEY ON FURNISHINGS OR GETTING IN A COUPLE OF COMPUTERS... IN THE END OUR CANDIDATE JUSTIN HAD THE FINAL SAY...

Panel 3: HE HAS A LOT OF HIS POTENTIAL VOTERS COME TO SEE HIM HERE AND HE SAID IT WAS IMPORTANT TO BE ABLE TO CONDUCT DISCUSSIONS WITH THEM IN A RELAXED, COMFORTABLE ENVIRONMENT..

Panel 4: SO YOU GOT THE COMPUTERS SO HE COULD SKYPE THEM FROM HIS TOWN HOUSE IN CHELSEA...? / YES. HE LIKES TO BE ABLE TO LOOK PEOPLE IN THE EYE WHEN HE BULLSH*TS THEM... / YOUR JOB IN THE PUBLIC SECTOR WILL BE PERFECTLY SAFE...

Alex PEATTIE + TAYLOR

WHAT A MARATHON! I FEEL EXHAUSTED PHYSICALLY AND MENTALLY BUT I'M GLAD I GOT THROUGH IT...!

LONDON MARATHON RESULTS

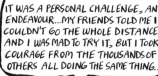

IT WAS A PERSONAL CHALLENGE, AN ENDEAVOUR...MY FRIENDS TOLD ME I COULDN'T GO THE WHOLE DISTANCE AND I WAS MAD TO TRY IT, BUT I TOOK COURAGE FROM THE THOUSANDS OF OTHERS ALL DOING THE SAME THING...

IN THE LATTER STAGES IT GOT A LITTLE DISPIRITING I MUST ADMIT.. THE WORST MOMENT WAS JUST AS I WAS NEARING THE END AND I STARTED BEING OVERTAKEN BY OTHER PEOPLE...

PEOPLE LIKE ME, YES...

THE PEOPLE WHO SENSIBLY WAITED FOR PLANES TO START FLYING AGAIN INSTEAD OF TREKKING HOME OVERLAND LIKE YOU...

OKAY, THAT'S HOW YOU TWO GOT BACK FROM EUROPE. NOW CAN I TELL MY LONDON MARATHON STORY?

NO FEAR.

Alex PEATTIE + TAYLOR

AIRPORT INFORMATION DESK

I'M STILL STUCK OUT HERE IN FLORIDA, CYRUS. THE EARLIEST FLIGHT HOME THEY CAN GET ME ON IS NEXT WEEK...

YOU'VE ALREADY MISSED A WHOLE WEEK'S WORK, MIKE. I'M GONNA HAVE TO TAKE IT OUT OF YOUR HOLIDAY ALLOWANCE...

THAT'S DISGRACEFUL... I'M JUST THE VICTIM OF THE TRAVEL CHAOS THAT'S RESULTED FROM THE RECENT UK FLIGHT BAN...

MIKE, YOU GOTTA LOOK AT IT FROM MY POINT OF VIEW... I'M YOUR BOSS AND MY ONLY CONCERN IS THE EFFECT THAT YOUR UNAUTHORIZED AND UNPLANNED-FOR ABSENCE IS HAVING ON THE RUNNING OF THIS DEPART-MENT...

NONE AT ALL AS FAR AS I CAN SEE.. IN FACT I'M STARTING TO WONDER WHY WE EVEN EMPLOY YOU...

OH CRIPES... LOOK, PUT IT DOWN AS A HOLIDAY AND I'LL BRIBE MY WAY ONTO A PLANE TOMORROW...

ATTA-BOY!

Alex PEATTIE + TAYLOR

SO YOU TOOK 4 DAYS TO GET BACK FROM ITALY LAST WEEK WHEN YOU COULD HAVE JUST WAITED FOR THE END OF THE FLIGHT BAN, TIM?

YOU MUST FEEL RATHER FOOLISH...

ACTUALLY, TRAVELLING ACROSS EUROPE BY LAND GAVE ME A REAL INSIGHT INTO A CONTINENT THAT'S RIVEN BY ECONOMIC DIVISIONS, ALEX...

THERE'S TALK THAT THE EURO MIGHT NOT SURVIVE. CERTAINLY THERE'S A MOOD OF NOSTALGIA FOR THE OLD NATIONAL CURRENCIES.. I SAW A LOT WHICH PUT ME IN MIND OF THOSE DAYS..

AH YES...

LIKE THIS MEGA-LONG STRING OF DIGITS ON YOUR TAXI BILL FROM MILAN TO BRUSSELS. REMINDS ME OF WHEN THEY HAD THE LIRA...GOOD LUCK GETTING THIS PAST CYRUS ON EXPENSES..

OO-ER...

Alex PEATTIE + TAYLOR

IT'S TRAGIC WHAT'S HAPPENING TO GREECE; BEING REDUCED TO THIS MESS...IT'S SUCH A HUMILIATION...

BUT WHAT CAN THEY DO?

GREEK BONDS DOWN-GRADE

I DON'T KNOW, BUT I'M A GREAT BELIEVER IN THE POWER OF PEOPLE'S MINDS TO WILL THINGS TO CHANGE... THEY NEED TO VISUALISE HOW THEIR ECONOMY MIGHT IMPROVE.

THEY SHOULD USE MENTAL ENERGY TO FOCUS ON THE MARKETS EACH MORNING AND TRY TO LIFT THEM BY THINKING POSITIVE THOUGHTS: "GREECE: UP... GREECE: UP..."

RIGHT...

AS IN "IF WE GREASE UP TO THE GERMANS ENOUGH MAYBE THEY'LL GIVE US A BAIL-OUT..." YES, THAT MIGHT WORK...

Alex PEATTIE + TAYLOR

KNOCKING ON DOORS IS STILL AN IMPORTANT PART OF CAMPAIGNING BUT ONE CAN'T NEGLECT THE USE OF TECHNOLOGY...

JUST ABOUT EVERYONE CONNECTED WITH THIS ELECTION HAS A TWITTER ACCOUNT AND IT'S IMPORTANT FOR US TO MONITOR WHAT'S BEING SAID BY OUR OPPONENTS AS WELL AS OUR SUPPORTERS...

ONE CAN'T DENY THAT THIS CAMPAIGN IS GETTING PERSONAL AND THE SORT OF INFORMATION PEOPLE DISCLOSE ON THESE NETWORKS CAN SOMETIMES WORK TO OUR ADVANTAGE...

JUSTIN...

HERE: MR BEESLEY AT NUMBER 35 TWEETS: "I'VE JUST RUN A NICE BATH AND I'M GETTING INTO IT..."

GOOD...

HE'S A LABOUR SUPPORTER WHO'S BEEN SLAGGING US OFF... LET'S GO AND RING HIS DOORBELL TO ANNOY HIM.

Alex PEATTIE + TAYLOR

IT'S VERY GOOD OF YOU TO DO SO MUCH TO HELP YOUR HUSBAND'S ELECTION CAMPAIGN...

HOW COULD I REFUSE?

A SUCCESSFUL CANDIDATE NEEDS A DUTIFUL WIFE BY HIS SIDE AND JUSTIN REALLY CARES PASSIONATELY ABOUT BECOMING AN M.P...

AND CONSIDERING ALL THE TIME AND EFFORT HE'S PUT INTO HIS CAMPAIGNING THE CONSEQUENCES OF HIM NOT WINNING DON'T BEAR THINKING ABOUT...

HE'D HAVE TO GO BACK TO WORK AT THE BANK, WHERE THE IDIOT HAS NOW USED UP ALL HIS HOLIDAY ALLOWANCE FOR THE YEAR...

AFTER ALL, I NEED MY FOUR WEEKS IN TUSCANY THIS SUMMER...

Alex PEATTIE + TAYLOR

I HOPE I WIN, ALEX. IT'D BE THE PERFECT TIME TO GET OUT OF BANKING AND INTO POLITICS...

I MEAN JUST LOOK AT THE LATEST ALLEGATIONS ABOUT THE CULTURE WITHIN INVESTMENT BANKS THAT HAVE COME FROM LAST WEEK'S SENATE HEARINGS IN THE U.S.A...

THE SUGGESTION IS THAT BANKERS ROUTINELY MISLEAD CUSTOMERS BY WITHHOLDING KEY INFORMATION FROM THEM AND TRYING TO SELL THEM PRODUCTS THAT DO NOT MATCH THEIR INTERESTS...

RIGHT...

SO: HAVE YOU TOLD VOTERS THAT YOU'RE PLANNING TO RAISE THEIR TAXES, SLASH PUBLIC SERVICES AND SACK PUBLIC SECTOR WORKERS?

ARE YOU CRAZY? I NEED THEM TO VOTE ME IN FIRST...

SOUNDS LIKE A GOOD SKILL FIT...

Alex PEATTIE + TAYLOR

THE QUESTION NOW IS WHETHER THE GREEK DEBT CRISIS CAN BE CONTAINED...

THERE ARE REAL FEARS THAT THE CONTAGION COULD NOW SPREAD TO OTHER EUROPEAN COUNTRIES IN A KIND OF CHAIN REACTION...

SO WE NEED TO FORMULATE A POLICY ON PORTUGAL, WHICH HAS SIMILAR DEBT PROBLEMS TO GREECE... AFTER ALL WE'D BE FOOLISH TO IGNORE THE LINKS HERE.

YES, WE WOULD...

PORTUGAL'S GOT SOME REALLY LOVELY LINKS

SO WE'LL ORGANISE AN URGENT FACT-FINDING TRIP. DON'T FORGET TO BRING YOUR CLUBS...

Alex PEATTIE + TAYLOR

I WAS TALKING TO OUR ESSEX TRADER FRIEND VINCE AND HE'S GIVEN ME RENEWED HOPE FOR MY CAMPAIGN.

YOU SEE COMPANIES LIKE HIS WHICH TAKE MARKET POSITIONS THAT COULD BE SIGNIFICANTLY AFFECTED BY THE ELECTION RESULT OFTEN COMMISSION THEIR OWN PRIVATE POLITICAL POLLS...

WELL, OFFICIALLY THE THREE MAIN CANDIDATES IN THIS CONSTITUENCY ARE NECK-AND-NECK, BUT VINCE SAID THAT ACCORDING TO HIS INFORMATION I SHOULD HAVE A SUBSTANTIAL EDGE...

REALLY?

SO YOU TOLD JUSTIN HE SHOULD HAVE A SUBSTANTIAL HEDGE, VINCE?

YEAH, IF HE'S GOT ANY SENSE HE'LL GO SHORT STERLING LIKE I HAVE... LOOKS LIKE A HUNG PARLIAMENT, WHICH MEANS THE U.K.'S ****ED...

Alex PEATTIE + TAYLOR

SO, JUSTIN, THE GENERAL ELECTION IS OVER AND YOU'RE BACK AT THE BANK...

WHAT COMES NEXT IS THE HARD BIT. IT'S GOING TO BE A REAL TEST OF YOUR CHARACTER. I KNOW IT WILL BE DIFFICULT FOR YOU TO SWALLOW YOUR PRIDE UNDER THE CIRCUMSTANCES,

BUT?

BUT THERE SHOULDN'T BE ANY BITTERNESS OR RECRIMINATIONS. TRY TO BE GRACIOUS, DIGNIFIED, PHILOSOPHICAL ABOUT WHAT'S HAPPENED... TAKE A LONG-TERM VIEW...

I KNOW YOU'RE RIGHT, ALEX, BUT I DON'T KNOW IF I CAN DO THAT..

HA HA! I WON, CYRUS! I'M AN M.P. NOW, SO I'M GOING TO TELL YOU WHERE YOU CAN STICK YOUR JOB!

OH DEAR...DOES HE NOT REALISE HE MAY NEED TO GROVEL FOR HIS JOB BACK SOON IF THERE'S A SECOND ELECTION AND HE GETS KICKED OUT?

Alex PEATTIE + TAYLOR

I'D HOPED IT WOULD ALL BE OVER BY POLLING DAY WITH THE ELECTION DELIVERING A CLEAR, DECISIVE RESULT...

BUT WITH THIS HUNG PARLIAMENT EVERYTHING'S STILL UP IN THE AIR AND WE'VE GOT TO CONTEND WITH A FRUSTRATING PERIOD OF CONTINUED UNCERTAINTY...

ALL THE WHEELER-DEALING, THE BEHIND-THE-SCENES MACHINATIONS AND MANOEUVRING AS THE VARIOUS FACTIONS TRY TO SHORE UP THEIR POSITIONS AND SECURE AN ADVANTAGE...

IT'S A NIGHTMARE...

BLOODY ON-LINE BETTING...IT'S RUINED MY DINNER PARTY...

DAYS TILL NEXT ELECTION: 72-85

MANDELSON TO BE NEXT P.M. 15-1

UK TO DEFAULT ON DEBT BY 2015: 6-1

BROWN TO RESIGN AND BECOME A MISSIONARY: 150-1...

Alex PEATTIE + TAYLOR

SO WITH NO CLEAR WINNER IN THE ELECTION IT'S NOW DOWN TO POLITICAL HORSE-TRADING TO SEE WHO RUNS THE COUNTRY.

IT'S ALREADY CLEAR THAT WE'RE NOT GOING TO SEE THE SWIFT, ROBUST, DECISIVE AND PRINCIPLED ECONOMIC ACTION BEING TAKEN THAT WE WERE PROMISED BEFORE THE ELECTION.

INSTEAD WE'RE GOING TO GET NOTHING BUT COMPROMISES, FUDGES, BACK-TRACKING, HALF-MEASURES AND WAIT-AND-SEE POLICIES...

DOES THAT REALLY SURPRISE YOU?

WELL, YES, ACTUALLY...

I MEAN, ALEX DEFINITELY SAID HE'D BE GOING OFF TO LIVE IN SWITZERLAND IF THE TORIES DIDN'T GET AN OVERALL MAJORITY...

OH, WE ALL KNEW THAT WAS A BLUFF...

I THINK IT'S IMPORTANT TO BIDE ONE'S TIME...

alex@alexcartoon.com

Alex PEATTIE + TAYLOR

SO ONE OF OUR CLIENTS GOT FIRED AND WE'RE GOING TO INTERVIEW HIM FOR A JOB HERE?

YES.

WE'RE JUST GOING THROUGH THE MOTIONS, CLIVE. WE'VE NO INTENTION OF EMPLOYING HIM... IT'S JUST SO HE'LL THINK WELL OF US IF HE ENDS UP AS OUR CLIENT AGAIN ONE DAY...

BUT, ALEX, HOW CAN WE TURN HIM DOWN?

WE'VE ALWAYS SUCKED UP TO HIM, FLATTERED HIS EGO, ENCOURAGED HIM TO BELIEVE HE'S A GENIUS AND PRETENDED TO BE DAZZLED BY HIS INTELLECT AND INSIGHT. THIS IS ALL GOING TO BACKFIRE ON US NOW

ON THE CONTRARY...

IT MEANS THE CONCEITED IDIOT MIGHT ACTUALLY BELIEVE US WHEN WE RELUCTANTLY CONCLUDE THAT HE'S "OVERQUALIFIED" TO PERFORM OUR LOWLY ROLE...

THAT'S COMFORTING...

Alex PEATTIE + TAYLOR

SO WE'VE GOT TO INTERVIEW AN EX-CLIENT FOR A JOB?

WELL HE RECENTLY GOT MADE REDUNDANT, CLIVE...

SO WE'RE GIVING HIM AN INTERVIEW JUST TO LOOK GOOD IN HIS EYES IN CASE HE GETS A NEW JOB AND BECOMES OUR CLIENT AGAIN...

A GOOD THING TOO... HE'S AN ARROGANT TWERP...

I HATE THE WAY WE ALWAYS HAVE TO KOWTOW TO CLIENTS LIKE HIM AND EAT HUMBLE PIE... WELL, THE BOOT'S ON THE OTHER FOOT NOW AS WE CAN SUBJECT HIM TO ALL THE RIGOURS OF A FORMAL JOB INTERVIEW...

SO, GIVE ME AN EXAMPLE OF A TIME WHEN YOU SHOWED INITIATIVE...

LAST YEAR, WHEN MY CORPORATE ADVISORS, IE: YOU, RECOMMENDED I GOT INTO GREEK BONDS AND I REFUSED...

AHEM... OH YES... SORRY ABOUT THAT..

Alex PEATTIE + TAYLOR

A LOT OF PEOPLE ARE VERY ANGRY ABOUT THIS NEW SERIES OF STRIKES BY B.A. CABIN STAFF OVER PROPOSED CUTBACKS...

YES.

IT'S THEIR SHEER INGRATITUDE THAT GETS ME... THEY REALLY ARE TOTALLY OUT OF TOUCH... THEY ENJOY VERY HIGH WAGES BY INDUSTRY STANDARDS AND THEY GET ALL SORTS OF ADDED LIFESTYLE PERKS...

YET SUCH IS THEIR COMPLACENCY AND SENSE OF ENTITLEMENT THAT THEY THROW A STROP AS SOON AS ANYONE THREATENS TO TAKE AWAY ANY ELEMENT OF THEIR GENEROUS JOB PACKAGE...

I KNOW WHAT YOU MEAN...

BLOODY BANKERS.

I'VE ALREADY MISSED OUT ON ENOUGH BUSINESS TRIPS DUE TO BLASTED VOLCANIC ASH... IF THIS GOES ON I'LL LOSE MY GOLD FREQUENT FLYER CARD...

Alex PEATTIE + TAYLOR

I THOUGHT I'D ARRANGE FOR YOU TO HAVE DINNER WITH MY EX-COLLEAGUE JUSTIN WHO IS NOW A MEMBER OF PARLIAMENT, MR HARDCASTLE...

YOU THINK THIS COULD BE A GOOD OPPORTUNITY TO DO SOME BUSINESS?

AHEM... IT'S IMPORTANT NOT TO BE TOO BLATANT ABOUT THIS SORT OF ARRANGEMENT...

LET'S JUST SAY THAT WHEN A PERSON FINDS HIMSELF IN A POSITION OF POWER AND INFLUENCE HE IS ABLE TO DO DISCREET FAVOURS FOR AND ADVANCE THE BUSINESS INTERESTS OF HIS PREFERRED PROFESSIONAL ASSOCIATES...

HEE HEE... SOUNDS GOOD...

SO, ANY CHANCE OF GETTING ME A NON-EXECUTIVE DIRECTORSHIP OR SOME CONSULTANCY WORK? I'VE GOT TO SCRAPE BY ON A MEASLY MP'S SALARY, PLUS THEY'VE PUT THE KIBOSH ON ALL THE DECENT EXPENSES SCAMS...

ER... HOLD ON...

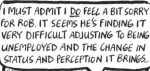

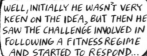

Alex PEATTIE+TAYLOR

I HAD LUNCH WITH ARCHIE THE P.R. MAN TODAY. DID YOU HEAR HE GOT MUGGED?

WHAT? WHEN...?

LAST NIGHT. HE WAS WALKING BACK FROM A CLIENT DINNER WHEN HE WAS CONFRONTED BY A THUG WHO FORCED HIM TO HAND OVER HIS WALLET AT KNIFEPOINT...

OH MY GOSH... WHAT AN AWFUL EXPERIENCE... HOW IS HE COPING?

HE SEEMED TO BE SUFFERING FROM DELAYED SHOCK... OBVIOUSLY HE FELT VIOLATED, DEGRADED, EMASCULATED: FINDING HIMSELF RENDERED HELPLESS AND VULNERABLE... HIS WHOLE EXISTENCE REDUCED TO NOTHING IN SOMEONE ELSE'S EYES...

THE MUGGER'S?

NO, MINE... WHEN THE RESTAURANT BILL CAME AND HE SUDDENLY REMEMBERED HE DIDN'T HAVE ANY CREDIT CARDS...

A P.R. MAN UNABLE TO PICK UP THE LUNCH TAB? IT'S UNTHINKABLE...

Alex PEATTIE+TAYLOR

I GOT A CALL OUT OF THE BLUE TODAY FROM AN EX-COLLEAGUE AT A BANK I USED TO WORK AT YEARS AGO

OH DEAR.

THAT USUALLY MEANS HE'S BEEN MADE REDUNDANT AND IS PHONING ROUND EVERYONE HE'S EVER KNOWN IN THE HOPE THAT THEY CAN SWING HIM A JOB WHERE THEY WORK...

TRUE...

BUT I WAS GLAD TO HEAR FROM HIM.

ONE OF THE NICE THINGS ABOUT BEING IN MY POSITION, HAVING HAD A SUCCESSFUL CAREER AND ACHIEVED A CERTAIN STATUS, IS WHAT ONE IS ABLE TO DO TO HELP AN OLD FRIEND IN NEED LIKE HIM...

RIGHT...

ABSOLUTELY NOTHING, AS YOU'RE RETIRED...

AND AT THE AGE OF 38 TOO. HE TOOK THE NEWS GRATIFYINGLY BADLY WHEN I TOLD HIM...

Alex PEATTIE+TAYLOR

SO, ROGER, AS THE BANK'S CHIEF ECONOMIST YOU'VE PRODUCED SOME RESEARCH ON THE WORLD CUP?

THAT'S RIGHT, ALEX. WE APPLIED SOME OF OUR ANALYTICAL MODELS TO THE TOURNAMENT AND CAME TO THE CONCLUSION THAT ENGLAND WILL WIN. IT WAS JUST A BIT OF FUN REALLY...

OBVIOUSLY ONE WOULDN'T WANT TO ENQUIRE TOO DEEPLY AS TO HOW RELEVANT A LIGHT-HEARTED EXERCISE LIKE THIS IS TO OUR _REAL_ JOB OF PRODUCING SERIOUS ECONOMIC RESEARCH.

NO OF COURSE NOT.

...RELYING ON BLIND OPTIMISM THAT FLIES IN THE FACE OF ALL REASON... IT'S EXACTLY _WHAT_ YOU DO ALL THE TIME...

WELL, WE HAVE TO BE UNREMITTINGLY BULLISH ON THE ECONOMY TO GET OUR CLIENTS TO DEAL...

Alex PEATTIE+TAYLOR

THERE ARE A LOT OF CONTINENTAL EUROPEANS WORKING IN THE CITY OF LONDON THESE DAYS...

IT'S HARDLY SURPRISING, CLIVE...

AFTER ALL THEY TEND TO STAY IN EDUCATION FOR MUCH LONGER THAN US, OFTEN ACQUIRING A COUPLE OF DEGREES AND PERHAPS EVEN A PhD BEFORE EMBARKING ON A CAREER...

THE EXTRA TIME DEVOTED TO ACADEMIA MEANS THEY'RE MORE MATURE - OFTEN IN THEIR LATE 20s WHEN THEY COME IN FOR INTERVIEW, WHICH HAS OBVIOUS ADVANTAGES FOR US AS EMPLOYERS...

YES...

IT'S SO DEPRESSING WHEN YOU REALISE THAT YOU'D ALREADY STARTED YOUR OWN CAREER WHEN THE PERSON YOU'RE INTERVIEWING WAS BORN...

QUITE. SO ANY OPPORTUNITY TO STAVE OFF THAT GRIM REALITY...

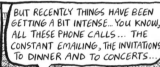

Alex PEATTIE + TAYLOR

SO YOU'RE PLANNING TO TAKE CHRISTOPHER AND HIS GIRLFRIEND TO WIMBLEDON?

I THOUGHT IT MIGHT HELP THEIR RELATIONSHIP, PENNY...

RUBBISH... I BET YOU'RE ONLY INVITING HER ON THE CONDITION THAT SHE BRINGS HER DAD, WHO YOU'RE TRYING TO WOO AS A CLIENT...

THERE'S SOME TRUTH IN THAT...

REALLY, ALEX... HOW UTTERLY CYNICAL AND SELF-SERVING CAN YOU GET? IS THERE ANYONE YOU WOULDN'T MANIPULATE, EXPLOIT OR SACRIFICE TO FURTHER YOUR BUSINESS INTERESTS?

SO, DAD, WHAT DO WE DO WHEN MUM WORKS OUT THAT I'LL BE GOING TO THE MEN'S FINAL IN PLACE OF HER?

WE'LL WORRY ABOUT THAT WHEN WE COME TO IT, CHRISTOPHER.

Alex PEATTIE + TAYLOR

SOPHIE'S FATHER JUST PHONED ME ABOUT CHRISTOPHER TAKING HER AWAY ON FRIDAY...

YES. I HEARD YOU TALKING TO HIM...

I KNOW HE'S A CEO AND EVERYTHING, PENNY, BUT ONE MUST REMEMBER HE'S ALSO A CONCERNED PARENT WORRIED ABOUT HIS DAUGHTER... I THINK I MANAGED TO REASSURE HIM.

POOR SOPHIE... I FEEL SORRY FOR HER.

WHY?

WHEN YOU'RE IN A RELATIONSHIP AND IT'S STILL EARLY DAYS YOU DON'T REALLY WANT YOUR DAD ASKING INTRUSIVE QUESTIONS ABOUT WHAT STAGE YOU'RE AT, DO YOU?

HELLO, SOPHIE, WHAT STAGE ARE YOU AT?
ER,...THE ACOUSTIC STAGE, DADDY...

I'M IN A CORPORATE WINNEBAGO WITH CHRISTOPHER'S DAD... WHY DON'T WE HOOK UP...?

GLASTONBURY

GRR...

Alex PEATTIE + TAYLOR

YOU KNOW, FRANCIS, YOU'RE PROBABLY THE ONLY PERSON I KNOW WHO'S BEEN 100% BULLISH THROUGHOUT THE RECENT FINANCIAL CRISIS...

WELL, ALEX, I'VE ALWAYS ADVISED MY CLIENTS THAT GLOBAL EQUITIES ARE FUNDAMENTALLY SOUND AND ANY FALL IN THE MARKET REPRESENTS A STRONG BUYING OPPORTUNITY...

RIGHT...

BUT FRANKLY NO ONE CAN IGNORE THE WORSENING ECONOMIC DATA AND LIKE A GOOD STOCK-BROKER I'VE ADJUSTED MY VIEWPOINT ACCORDINGLY...

SO I'M NOW 100% BEARISH AND TELLING MY CLIENTS TO SELL EVERYTHING.

WELL, NO POINT IN MESSING AROUND IN THE MIDDLE GROUND... YOU NEED TO GET THEM DEALING AND GENERATE YOURSELF SOME COMMISSION...

Alex PEATTIE + TAYLOR

SO HOW ARE THINGS GOING WITH SOPHIE, CHRISTOPHER? DO YOU THINK SHE MIGHT BE THE ONE FOR YOU?

LIKE YOU REALLY *CARE* ABOUT ME OR HER, DAD?

ALL YOU'RE THINKING ABOUT IS YOUR OWN INTERESTS AND TRYING TO INGRATIATE YOURSELF WITH HER DAD BECAUSE HE'S A COMPANY CEO AND YOU WANT HIM TO BE YOUR CLIENT...

WELL I DON'T CARE ABOUT SOPHIE'S DAD... I ONLY CARE ABOUT *HER*... I JUST WANT WHAT'S BEST FOR *HER*... CAN YOU UNDERSTAND THAT?

YES, OF COURSE

SO WHY DON'T I GET HER AN INTERNSHIP AT THE BANK? GOOD THINKING, CHRISTOPHER. THAT SHOULD PLEASE THE OLD BOY...

AARGH...

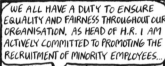

Alex PEATTIE + TAYLOR

THE GREAT FEAR AT THE MOMENT IS THE ECONOMY TIPPING DOWN AGAIN AND THEN WE'D GET THE "DOUBLE DIP" OR SO-CALLED "W"-SHAPED RECESSION.

YES, BUT THE FINANCIAL COMMUNITY IS USUALLY FIRST IN AND FIRST OUT OF ANY TREND AND THEY SEEM TO BE SHOWING THE WAY...

UK BUSINESSES MAY STILL BE UNCERTAIN ABOUT WHAT FORM OF RECOVERY TO LOOK FOR, BUT WHAT THEY'RE GETTING FROM THE BANKS IS A VERY CLEAR SIGN...

WHAT, THE CLASSIC "V", YOU MEAN?

EXACTLY.

AS IN: "EFF-OFF. WE'RE NOT LENDING YOU ANY MONEY"?

YES. IT'S STILL EVERY MAN FOR HIMSELF, I'M AFRAID...

Alex PEATTIE + TAYLOR

CLIVE, ARE YOU GOING TO SPEND YOUR ENTIRE HOLIDAY ON SOCIAL NETWORKING WEBSITES?

BUT, BRIDGET...

YOU DON'T UNDERSTAND HOW INTEGRAL FACEBOOK, TWITTER ETC ARE TO PEOPLE'S LIVES THESE DAYS...IT'S IMPORTANT TO UPDATE YOUR STATUS TO LET EVERY- BODY KNOW WHERE YOU ARE, WHAT YOU'RE DOING AND SO FORTH...

IT'S RIDICULOUS... WHAT'S THE POINT IN HAVING PAID A FORTUNE TO RENT THIS ELEGANT SPACIOUS VILLA IN THE TUSCAN HILLS IF YOU'RE NOT GOING TO MAKE PROPER USE OF IT?

...I.E: BY TELLING PEOPLE ABOUT IT... INSTEAD OF CLAIMING WE'RE BACK HOME HAVING A "STAYCATION"...

BUT I'VE HEARD THAT BURGLARS USE FACEBOOK TO TARGET THE HOUSES OF PEOPLE WHO ARE AWAY...

Alex PEATTIE + TAYLOR

THE CONSENSUS IN THE FINANCIAL WORLD IS THAT ECONOMIC CATASTROPHE HAS BEEN AVERTED, BUT THE OUTLOOK'S HARDLY CHEERY...

THE MOST OPTIMISTIC FORECAST IS THAT THINGS WILL BE FLAT FOR THE NEXT FEW YEARS BUSINESS-WISE AS GOVERNMENTS IMPLEMENT AUSTERITY MEASURES AND COMPANIES AND INDIVIDUALS RETRENCH...

OF COURSE THIS DOESN'T HAVE THE SAME SIGNIFICANCE FOR SOMEONE LIKE YOU, RUPERT. YOU'RE OF AN OLDER GENER- ATION. YOU MADE YOUR MONEY IN THE BOOM YEARS AND YOU'RE NOW ON THE VERGE OF RETIREMENT...

QUITE...

AND SO THIS WOULD BE THE PERFECT TIME FOR ME TO WORK ON MY KNIGHTHOOD BY SITTING ON LOADS OF QUANGOS...

EXCEPT THE GOVERNMENT'S CURRENTLY ABOLISHING THEM ALL...

IT'S MOST ANNOYING...

Alex PEATTIE + TAYLOR

SO HOW DID YOU ENJOY WORKING AT THE BANK OVER THE SUMMER, SOPHIE?

WELL IT WAS A CHALLENGE, ALEX.

AT THE BEGINNING I FELT TOTALLY OUT OF MY DEPTH. I DIDN'T KNOW HOW TO DO ANYTHING...I DIDN'T UNDERSTAND THE FIRST THING ABOUT BANKING... I FELT I WAS THE STUPIDEST AND MOST USELESS PERSON IN THE CITY...

BUT THEN MY CONFIDENCE WAS REALLY BOOSTED AT THE END OF MY LAST WEEK WHEN I GOT A PHONE CALL FROM A HEAD- HUNTER TRYING TO POACH ME...

AH YES,

IT MUST HAVE BEEN COMFORTING TO REALISE THERE WAS SOMEONE EVEN MORE CLUELESS THAN YOU OUT THERE... I IMAGINE HE GOT YOUR NAME FROM THE BANK'S EMAIL DIRECTORY...

HE DID SEEM EMBARRASSED WHEN I EXPLAINED I WAS JUST AN UNPAID INTERN...

ALEX WENT ON HOLIDAY TO SPAIN...

ALEX TAKES THE MIC ON CLASSIC *fm*

**Every Sunday evening at 7 pm investment banker Alex Masterley plays
his favourite classical recordings and shares his outspoken opinions.**

Starting September 12ᵗʰ 2010